D1226918

LETTERS TO
SMOKEY
BEAR

Edited by BILL ADLER

**Pictures by
SUSAN PERL**

GROSSET & DUNLAP • NEW YORK

Library of Congress Catalog Card Number: 66-14302

© 1966, by Bill Adler

Dear Smokey,

   I colored a picture
of you.

   I colored you green. Did you ever
see a green bear? You looked terrific.
I think green bears would be
very popular.

   I colored you green because
     I didn't have any crayon.

              Love,

                Marsha W.
                NYC

Dear Smokey,

Please send me ten Smokey the Bear
kits, I am starting a Smokey the Bear
club.

Could I have the kits by June 5 at
3 p.m. That is the time of our first
meeting. Please don't let the kits be
late because I am Club President and I
start my meetings right on time.

Love,
Agnes W.
Houston, Texas

Dear Smokey
    You mistaked.
I asked for 50 badges.
You only sent me one.

            Mickey K.
Cleveland, Ohio

Dear Smokey Bear
   I would like to
have a Junior Fire
Fighting kit.
   I have been waiting
for two years and I am
not getting any younger.
   Your fire fighting
helper Cindy C.
Portland, Oregon

Hi Smokey Bear.

I took matches away from my little brother because he tried to lite a paper bag on fire, and I spanked his hand.

Your Pal
Robin H.
Anderson,
Indiana.

Dear Smokey,

    I hope that you are okay. Do you have a picture of you when you were a little bear?

    Here is a picture of me when I was a little boy.

    Wasn't I cute? I'll bet you were cute too. Please send me a picture so I can see.

Good by

Love

Paula

Greenville,
   North Carolina

Dear Smokey,

On January 3rd it wasn't cold at all
but then I saw a man who was smoking a cigar.
I watched him for a long time and then he
threw it down.

I went over and said "Mister you
forgot to put out your cigar." He said,
"Aw shut up."

Before I knew it part of the grass
was burning. I saw a hose and put it out.
The woman thanked me.

End of story.

Your pal,

Red M.

Louisville, Kentucky

Dear smokey
I am not
doing so good
in being a
ranger.
There is no
trees so I can
not put
them out.

Love,
Bruce
Levittown
New York

Dear Smokey and friends,

I would like information about
Smokey and his wild friends.

Because you see I love animals very
much and would like to protect them
from fire.

I always liked animals and I always will. I will try my best to
keep their lovely homes from burning.

Yours truly,

Mark D.

Kenvil, New Jersey

P.S. No grownup helped me with this
letter. I wrote it by myself.

Dear Smokey,

We sang your song in our class. Everybody sang the Smokey song very well except Richard. He is always flat. He should sing in a whisper.

Yours truly,
Daniel S.
Liberty Center
Ohio

Dear Smokey,

I think that animals should have privilage to live just as us humans do. Poor animals are driven out of there homes just for highways.

Animals should have the privilage to live in this world. After all they own part of it. But people just drive them out of their own land.

If I had my way animals would live peacefully in forests and in our homes.

Sincerely,
Theresa H.
Meredith, N.H.

Dear Smokey,
   I would Like
To buy a Smokey
bear Forest Ranger
hat.
   I wear a size
6 1/4 or 5 1/4 or 5 1/2 hat.
You better send
all three. I Never
remember my right
size

          A Pal
          RANDY T.
          Montebello Calif

Dear Smokey –

In my Junior Forest Ranger kit you
sent me there was a Junior Forest Ranger
badge.

The next day when I wore it, it fell
off my blouse and some one stepped on it.
I didn't get there name or I would have
called the police.

They should put people like that in
jail.

Your fan,
Delores J.
NYC

Dear Smokey,

Just a few lines to let you know
that I read the book about you and about
your mother.

I will tell all the grown ups not
to drop fire in the forest and burn trash
when it is winded.

I will burn my trash when the
wind is not blew.

I am closed my letter

Mike K.

Chicago

Dear Smokey,
   I, Jeffrey, want to be a member of the Smokey the Bear Club.
   I, Jeffrey, am 9 years old.
   I, Jeffrey, am very strong and can be a big help.
   I, Jeffrey, must sign off now.
      Love from me,
   Jeffrey, Chicago

Dear Smokey Bear,
I would like
to be a Junior
Forest Ranger.
I am in kinder
garten. My brother
wrote this letter
but I told him
what to say.
My brother is
in the second
grade. He is a
genius. Love,
David G.
Hartford, Conn

Dear Smokey,

     I have sent you this small
cake of soap because nobody likes
a dirty bear.

            Your friend,

            Irving L.

            Atlanta,Georgia

P.S. I hope that you are not in-
sulted. I know that you are a
clean bear. You can give the soap
to any bear friends you have that
are not as clean as you.

Dear Smokey,

I am writing to let you know that
no one can join our club unless they
can tell the password -- <u>Smokey</u>.

Our club slogan is - Don't take
nothing but pictures out of the forests
or parks and leave nothing but foot prints
when you leave thé forest or park.

We say our club slogan every
day but Sunday. Sunday we say our
prayers in church.

Love,

Peter H.

Albany, N.Y.

Dear Smokey,

I wish I could be a Junior Forest Ranger.
I would like to help by preventing forest fires and by helping my little brother out of the match box.
Good luck.

Your friend,
John M.
Muncie, Indiana

Dear Smokey
I think your
kind of cute.
I'll bet you
have a lot of
bear girl
friends.

love
Mary Ann
New port
News, Va.

Dear Smokey,

I would like to be in your club.
I know the Conservation Pledge by heart.

I want to prevent forest fires.
I have planted grass, flowers, trees and
tomatoes.

Once I helped a bird that was sick
and hurt and it lived.

Once our dryer was on fire and I
helped put it out.

As you can see I am a very nice kid.

Yours,

Alice Z.

Arlington, Virginia

Hi Smokey,

EVERY time WE
SEE SMOKE THAT
ISN'T FROM A CHIMNEY
WE RUSH TO WHERE
IT COMES FROM.

I AM going To do
ALL I CAN To PREVENT
FIRE IN THE gulch
behind MY house.

Your PAL
BRUCE R.
CLEVELAND, OHIO

Dear Smokey,

I would like to be a Junior Forest Ranger and my friends want to be one, too.

We would like 5 membership cards for Marsha, Hilda, Ruth and myself, Mickey.

We have started a club. Our club will meet in my house except when my mother yells and then we will meet o utside.

Yo ur good friend,

Mickey K.

Bedford, N.H .

Hi Smokey,

This is Betsy Roberts again. Do you
remember getting a letter from Hilda Lang?
Well she is my friend. She came over to my
house while I was writing your last letter.
She asked me who I was writing to. I told
her about the Junior forest rangers and showe
her my kit. She wanted one. She got it toda
I have been hanging my things up in my room.
I have been asking people to join the Junior
Forest Rangers.

So far I have 4 that said yes. So
you might be getting 4 more letters.

If you want lots more letters please
let me know.

Love,

Rita G.

Chicago, Ill.

Dear Smokey
You are the bravest
bear I ever read
            about.
You are so brave
I almost thought
you were a lion.
        Sincerely yours,
        Linda J
    Tucson, Arizona

DEAR Smokey,

I think that I should be in your Junior Ranger club because i have taken in a stray cat and once a dog and saved a child from being burned playing with matches.

Don't you think i deserve to Be in your club??

Sincerely,
Mike W.
Atlanta, Georgia

Dear Smokey Bear,

I wish you could come and see me.

I know that you are happy in the
zoo in Washington but maybe they will
give you a vacation from the zoo so
you can visit me.

I think it would be a good idea
because our doctor says that everybody
needs a vacation.

Your pal

Debby D.

Las Vegas, Nevada

Hi Smokey,
My name is
Jeffrey. I
quit playing
the violin.
Now I want
to be a for-
est ranger.
A pal,
Terry H.
Pike
New Hampshire

Dear Smokey:

I am preventing Fires and if you can send me some tools and fire extinguisher for putting out fires I will make New York safe from all fires

Yours Sincerely,

Hank W.
N.Y.C.

Dear Smokey,

How are you? What do you do in your spare time?

Do you have a lot of friends? What is your favorite game? My favorite game is jump rope. Can bears jump rope?

Please answer my important questions.

I am writing this letter in the kitchen. I am drinking a glass of chocolate milk.

I can write but I like to print.

I love you,
Sandra W.
Salt Lake City, Utah

Dear Smokey,

    You are the most loveable
bear in the whole world.

    I would sure like to meet
you so I can hug you and kiss
you.

    My girl friend Jennifer
wants to hug you and kiss you
too because she thinks you are
the most loveable bear in the
whole world too.

                    Your friend,

                    Cecilia W.

                    San Francisco

Dear Smokey
I am a Junior
forest ranger
but I have to
move.
There are never
any forest fires
in Brooklyn.
Love
Janet L.

Dear Smokey

Thank you for sending me my badges because it has been raining and theres been no fires.

Rep W

Philadelphia

Dear Smokey,

I like all the animals of the
forest very much.

My favorite animal of the
forest is the chipmunk.

I hope some day the chipmunk
can get to be king of the forest
because chipmunks never get a chance
to be boss.

Yours,

Sherman J.

Detroit, Michigan

Dear Smokey,

Our class of second grade students is presenting a play about Smokey Bear.

I was picked to play you. I hope I do a good job so you will be proud of me.

My first line in the play is "Only you can prevent forest fires."

I hope that I don't forget it. I am very nervous.

Mark J.

Los Angeles, Calif.

dear Smokey bear,

I would like to have all the things in the Smokey Bear Junior Forest Ranger kit.

Please sen me two of everything because I am always losing things. Your friend
Rod S.
Casper, Wyoming

Dear Sirs
    I would like
to baby sit for
smokey.
    I am nine
years old and I
am not afraid
of bears.
        your freend
        Rhoda G.
allentown, Pa.

Dear Smokey,

My big brother is a Boy Scout. He told me not to play with matches.

You would like my big brother. He is very smart and we never fight except sometimes.

Love,
Rosemary L.
N.Y.C.

Dear Smokey Bear,

    I want to be a Forest Ranger like you.
I am against fire and for trees and so I
want to help.

    My mother wrote this letter for me
because I don't write so good and you
wouldn't know what I said and this is a
very important letter.

                        Your Pal,
                        John H.
                        Washington, D.C.

Dear Smokey,

   I like you very much. I've got a fire engine to help you put out fires.

   Please call me to help you because my fire engine isn't very busy.

          Your little
          Forest Ranger,

          Gregory B.
          Crestview,
          Florida

Dear Smokey,

It sure would be terrific if I could meet you in person except I wouldn't know what to say. I never talked to a bear before.

Love,
Janet W.
Birmingham,
Alabama